The BATHROOM BRAIN TEASERS BOOK

—— • ——

by

Russ Edwards & Jack Kreismer

RED-LETTER PRESS, INC.
Saddle River, New Jersey

THE BATHROOM BRAIN TEASERS BOOK

COPYRIGHT ©2011 Red-Letter Press, Inc.
ISBN-13: 978-1-60387-000-9
ISBN-10: 1-60387-000-8

Red-Letter Press, Inc.
P.O. Box 393
Saddle River, NJ 07458

www.Red-LetterPress.com

ACKNOWLEDGMENTS

EDITORIAL:
Jeff Kreismer

•

BOOK DESIGN AND TYPOGRAPHY:
Matt Taets

•

COVER:
Behum Graphics

•

CONTRIBUTORS:
Cristina Eichler
Eric Lehmann

•

PROJECT DEVELOPMENT:
Kobus Reyneke

The
BATHROOM
BRAIN TEASERS
BOOK

———— • ————

RED-LETTER PRESS, INC.
Saddle River, New Jersey

PENGUIN PUZZLER

Quinn the Eskimo was quite the hunter. He was pretty good at shooting off at the mouth, too. Not only would he tell you about his latest conquest; he'd tell you every little detail about the critter he bagged. That's just what he was doing at the local tavern one cold, wintry North Pole night.

"I'm tellin' you, Sal," Quinn said to the bartender, "I nabbed me an emperor penguin- had to be around 90 lbs. That's as big as they come. You know, them penguins are the only birds that can swim, but can't fly," said the Eskimo, explaining his catch while all the while demonstrating detailed knowledge of his prey.

"Oh, yeah," said Sal, visibly unimpressed.

"That's right," the Eskimo replied. "And this one was in the water when I got 'im. He was in a colony. That's what they call a group of penguins, ya know."

"Yeah, I know- I know a thing or two about penguins, too," said Sal. "And I know you didn't catch one."

Sal was right. Quinn wasn't only shooting off at the mouth- he put his foot in it this time. Can you explain?

PENGUIN PUZZLER (ANSWER)
Quinn the Eskimo lives at the North Pole. Penguins live in the Southern Hemisphere.

□   □   □

SIGN LANGUAGE

Are you a "roads scholar"? If so, there should be no trouble in spotting what's wrong with these interstate highway signs...

I-98 South

I-47 West

I-82 North

Answers on Page 10

Classic Conundrums

What's the only thing that's eaten before it is born and after it is dead?

A chicken

PURR-PLEXING

A well-dressed fellow parks his car, gets out, makes sure all the doors and windows are locked, and even checks to make certain that the trunk is not open. He goes about his business and when he returns a few minutes later, he finds a cat nestled up fast asleep on the back seat. How did the cat manage to get into the car?

◻   ◻   ◻

HUNTING FOR AN ANSWER?

Jack shot not one, not two, but three- count 'em - three eagles on that crisp autumn afternoon! Though he knew his wife wouldn't be particularly proud of what he'd done, his buddies were in awe of the achievement- shooting three eagles without killing a single one. How is that possible?

◻   ◻   ◻

MISS DAISY'S DRIVING

Daisy's car is parked on the street facing north. She gets in, takes off and drives along the street for a mile, winding up a mile south from her original starting point. What happened here?

SIGN LANGUAGE (ANSWER)
Interstate highways running north-south have odd numbers and have even numbers if running east-west.

PURR-PLEXING (ANSWER)
It was a convertible.

HUNTING FOR AN ANSWER? (ANSWER)
He eagled three holes in a round of golf.

MISS DAISY'S DRIVING (ANSWER)
She was driving in reverse.

Classic Conundrums
When you have me, you like to share me.
Then again, if you share me, you don't have me.
What am I?   A secret

IF LOOKS COULD KILL

Identical twins Bart and Art have frequented Benny's Bar by the Bay for years, always making their daily visit together at the same exact time. Bart has become rather friendly with Benny the Bartender. Art, meanwhile, has managed to get on Benny's bad side- and that's putting it rather mildly. You see, Benny is not a very patient person, nor does he enjoy mindless chatter. Whenever the twins stop in, Bart quickly exchanges pleasantries, orders and finishes a drink in under a minute, and is on his merry way. While Art doesn't have much to say either, that does not stop him. With each visit, he never fails to divert Benny's attention from his other customers and annoy everyone with his incessant babbling. To make matters worse, it takes Art nearly an hour to get through one measly cocktail. He continually overstays his welcome while costing Benny business at the same time.

After one particularly bad day, Benny decides he's had more than enough, and begins to devise a plan to put an end to Art's shenanigans once and for all. Thanks in part to his bartending expertise, he is quickly able to figure a way to poison Art. In fact, while he cannot tell the twins apart by their looks, he won't even have to wait for Art to start rambling during his next visit before he targets his victim. He will simply poison both of the twins' drinks, and is sure that Art will be the only one to suffer. When the two come in the following day, Benny takes action. He simultaneously hands Bart and Art their usual drinks, which are the same size, include the same amount of ice, and the same amount of poison. Sure enough, Benny walks away, unharmed, while Art is not so fortunate. How did Benny succeed with his plan?

IF LOOKS COULD KILL (ANSWER)
Benny put the poison in the ice. Because Bart drank
fast, his ice never melted, and no harm was done.
When Art took his grand ole' time as usual, he
ended up drinking the poison.

Rhyme Time

Often talked of, never seen,
Ever coming, never been.
Daily looked for, never here,
Still approaching, coming near.
Though they expect me to appear,
They will never find me here.

What am I?

Tomorrow (or the future)

PING PONG PROBLEM

You're proud of your finished basement and your new rec room. The construction is nearly finished when you invite your buddies over for a ping-pong match. The play is fast and furious all evening long and you are down to the game that will determine the winner. Then, disaster strikes! Your last usable ping-pong ball bounces down a narrow pipe embedded in concrete in the basement floor left over from the construction. The only tools you have at hand are a tape measure, a blowtorch, a nail gun, your bottle of drinking water, a drinking straw, two 9-Volt batteries, a pack of chewing gum, a tire patch kit, a length of twine, a bar of soap and a pair of pliers. How would you manage to retrieve the ball undamaged so you could get back to your game?

◻   ◻   ◻

THREE CARD DRAW

Three cards are face down on the table. A Diamond is to the left of a Heart. A Five is to the right of the Jack. A King is to the left of the Spade. A Spade is to the left of the Heart.

Name the three cards.

PING PONG PROBLEM (ANSWER)
You uncap your drinking water and pour it down
the pipe. The ball will float to the top. Dry it off and
you're ready to serve.

THREE CARD DRAW (ANSWER)
King of Diamonds, Jack of Spades, Five of Hearts

MAN ON THE GO #1

A Ferry Bad Dream

Old Stosh had been at his night watchman post for many years. He was a good watchman, but had learned where he could cut corners to make his life easier.

One evening, quite late, he spotted Mr. Schnizel, head of building security, stepping out of the elevator into the lobby.

"Working late I see, Mr. Schnizel," Stosh observed.

"Yeah, I'm going up to a security convention in Canada tomorrow and I had some work to finish before I left," Schnizel answered.

Surprised, Stosh asked, "How were you planning on going?"

"I just thought I'd drive up and take the ferry," Schnizel replied.

"Oh no, you mustn't," Stosh blurted out, ashen faced.

"And why not?"

"Because I had a dream about you last night. You were riding a big boat and it sunk," Stosh explained.

"Well, thanks for the tip, but you can't really believe in dreams, can you?" he said as he went out the door.

On his way home, Schnizel obsessed over Stosh's warning. Deciding not to tempt fate, he took a train in the morning. When he arrived, he heard everyone at the station talking about the ferry that had sunk- the one he was supposed to be on!

When Schnizel returned, he ran in and gave Stosh a big hug, a $10,000 reward and then fired him on the spot. Why did he fire him?

A Ferry Bad Dream (Answer)
Stosh had told Schnizel that he had a dream about him last night, so he was fired for sleeping on the job.

□   □   □

A Friendly Encounter

Trixie was shopping at Toys For Boys when she ran into an old friend.

"Oh, I see you have a family now," Trixie said as she smiled at her friend's little boy.

"Yes, I got married 8 years ago. Hey, we should get together sometime. I'd love for you to meet my significant other."

Trixie said, "That would be nice. Say, what's your son's name?"

"It's the same as Daddy's," replied her friend.

"Well, hello Eddie. It's nice to meet you."

How did Trixie know the boy's name?

Classic Conundrums

They can be made and they can be laid. They can be bent and they can be broken. But they cannot be touched. What are they? Rules

GOODBYE, MR. BLOND

In the new James Blond movie, *Thunderfinger*, there's a scene where Blond is captured by the super villain and locked in a stony dungeon cell with no metal in it except for two identical keys. All his spy gadgets have been taken away and he's on his own without so much as an exploding cufflink.

Like all good movie super villains, rather than killing Blond right away as soon as he has him in his clutches, Thunderfinger monologues for a while, telling Blond all his plans, and then leaves him to some overly contrived but "fitting" end.

In this case, Thunderfinger is feeling generous and decides to give Blond a sporting 50-50 chance.

If Blond inserts the magnetic key into the door, it will open and he'll only have to deal with the 500 guards in the dungeon passageway. If he inserts the other key, however, it will explode with the force of a half-ton of TNT.

We all know that 500 heavily armed guards would hardly ruffle the lapels on Blond's Savile Row suit, but how did he know which key to use?

A FRIENDLY ENCOUNTER (ANSWER)
Trixie's friend was a guy.

GOODBYE, MR. BLOND (ANSWER)
He removed a shoelace and hung a key on it, perfectly balanced. When he found the one that pointed north like a compass needle, he knew he had the right one.

Rhyme Time

I can sizzle like bacon,
I am made with an egg,
I have plenty of backbone,
But lack a good leg.
I peel layers like onions,
But still remain whole,
I can be long like a flagpole,
Yet fit in a hole.
What am I?

A snake

ANAGRAMS

Proofreaders hate these because they are supposed to be a jumble of words and non-sensical phrases. The first part of each anagram is the clue, followed by the scrambled name of a celebrity after the hyphen. Your mission, should you decide to accept it, is to re-jigger the letters and find the famous figure.

1. Long gone rock star- Mr. Mojo Risin'

2. Popular among friends- Fine in torn jeans

3. 43rd in a long line- He bugs Gore

4. Out of this world explorer- Mr. Strong Alien

5. Senior member of an acting brotherhood- Wild Balance

6. Mother of forceful rebellion- I loan apartment

7. Movie audiences have a strong bond with him- On any screen

8. Grins with a gap- Nerd amid late TV

9. Often scores with Burton- Flamed nanny

10. His theory was that it took a lot of energy to go to mass- Elite brain sent

ANAGRAMS (ANSWERS)

1. Jim Morrison

2. Jennifer Aniston

3. George Bush

4. Neil Armstrong

5. Alec Baldwin

6. Natalie Portman

7. Sean Connery

8. David Letterman

9. Danny Elfman

10. Albert Einstein

Classic Conundrums

You can hold it without using your hands or arms.
What is it?

Your breath

LAZING SADDLES

On this installment of Brainteasers of the Old West, we find aging cattle baron Chet Masterson talking to his two sons.

"Boys, I'm a headin' for the last roundup," he said as he knocked back a whiskey to wash the taste of the cigar out of his mouth. "I've pondered long and hard who to leave my vast fortune to. Nigh onto half the steers in Texas are under my brand and I've decided to leave it all to the winner of a horse race. Only this ain't no ordinary race, no siree! The one with the slowest horse gets to be the big he-bull around here. All the other one gets is my silver plated spittoon."

The rules of the contest required the boys to ride to the Texas border and then "race" back to the ranch house. At the starting pistol, each tried to ride slower than the other. After five days in the hot West Texas sun, they still found themselves wandering aimlessly around the desert. After they had passed his place for the twentieth time, an old sodbuster waved them over and asked them what in tarnation was going on. They explained everything to him, whereupon he thought for a moment and said something to the boys. Hearing this, they both took off at a full gallop towards home.

What did the old sodbuster say?

LAZING SADDLES (ANSWER)
He told them to switch horses.

❏   ❏   ❏

BRAIN TEASERS FOR YOUR INNER CHILD

What did the ancient Romans yell on the golf course?
"IV!"

How did the girl break off her relationship with the tractor salesman?
She sent him a John Deere letter.

What do you call a psychic dwarf that escapes from prison?
A small medium at large

What do you get if you cross an artist with a policeman?
A brush with the law

What do you get if you cross a Labrador retriever with a tortoise?
An animal that leaves and comes back with last week's newspaper

What do you get if you cross a cow with an octopus?
An animal that milks itself

What do you call a cow that's just had a baby?
De-calf-inated

THE SCRAMBLER - RIDDLES

The answers to these groaners are all provided for you. Simply unscramble the letters and re-arrange the words... ecka a ceepi fo (a piece of cake)!

1. What does a mobster buried in cement eventually become? **dehrande a mciirlna**

2. Why did the Siamese twins move to London?
    eth tohre evdir os neo lduco

3. How do you make gold soup?
    ni torarcs tpu ntereufo uyo.

4. What happened to the employees at the struggling sardine factory? **rwee nendac teyh.**

5. The answer is: Acoustic... And the question?
    lopo uyo twah od ot tohos seu?

6. What do you get when you cross a teacher with a vampire? **dlboo tols fo ttsse**

7. Why couldn't they play cards on Noah's ark?
    no tsa esucabe kdce tnpeelha eth het

8. What would you have if all the automobiles in America were pink? **rca nkip a ntnaio**

9. Why aren't kangaroos allowed to open bank accounts? **ccskeh swlaay enucob eriht.**

10. What did one toilet say to the other?
    "kolo dsluefh uyo."

THE SCRAMBLER - RIDDLES (ANSWERS)

1. A hardened criminal

2. So the other one could drive

3. You put in fourteen carrots.

4. They were canned.

5. What do you use to shoot pool?

6. Lots of blood tests

7. Because the elephant sat on the deck

8. A pink car nation

9. Their checks always bounce.

10. "You look flushed."

—— PHRASE CRAZE ——

Figure out the meaning of the term based upon the placement of the words.

GROPOOLUND

(Inground pool)

TIMING TIM ING

(Split second timing)

EINAR AND EOUTAR

(In one ear and out the other)

JUNKYARD WARS

Chopper and Louie worked at a junkyard and normally were the best of pals. Lately though, they had been getting on each other's nerves. Something had to give, and one day at lunch, it did.

Chopper, by far the larger of the two men, strode over to Louie and said, "Let's settle our differences with a bet. I bet you $100 that I can carry something in that wheelbarrow over there that you can't. Choose anything from the yard and push it. I say I can carry that and more."

Louie, who was built...well, like a guy named Louie, felt like he had to accept the bet and agreed.

"Anything you want, Louie," Chopper goaded him. "There's a Buick tranny over there, here's a stack of car batteries, an engine out of an '83 Ford. Grab anything you want for the wheelbarrow. You push it and I bet I can push it and a lot more."

What two words did Louie say to win the bet?

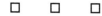

KEEPING SCORE

What's the one sport where neither the spectators nor participants know who's winning until the very end?

JUNKYARD WARS (ANSWER)
"Hop in."

KEEPING SCORE (ANSWER)
Boxing

─── **SIMPLE STUFF** ───

If a red house is made of red bricks, a white house is made of white bricks and a yellow house is made of yellow bricks, what is a greenhouse made of?

Glass

Which burns longer- a blue candle or a white candle?

Neither- They both burn shorter.

Classic Conundrums

*Even if you give it to someone else,
you still get to keep it. What is it?*

Your word

THE DATING GAME

It was 1957 and just about time for "The Summer Magic Under The Stars Dance", the biggest event of the year in Centerville.

Peggy Sue was the town's most popular bobby-soxer. Three of the town's best-looking boys had been pursuing her all year. All three had asked her to the dance.

Peggy Sue wanted to be fair, and since they were all equally handsome, she wanted to choose the smartest and sweetest guy. She set up a little contest and called them all to her living room.

"Boys," she told them, "I'll go to the dance with the one who brings me a gift small enough to fit in my purse, yet large enough to fill my living room. Now get on your way. I'll see you back here tomorrow at the same time. Good luck."

The next evening at the appointed time, the boys returned to Peggy Sue's living room. The first boy had brought some straw. It fit easily into her purse, but when laid out on the floor, it couldn't even begin to cover the area around the sofa.

The second boy had brought some very thin pieces of paper. Again, room to spare in the purse, but they hardly spread out any further than the straw.

The third boy placed his gift in her purse and proceeded to fill the room with it.

What did he bring to win the date to the big dance?

THE DATING GAME (ANSWER)
He brought a match. When struck, it filled the room with a romantic light.

MAN ON THE GO #2

I Spy

How observant are you? Do you notice details? Take this quiz to find out if you're closer to Sherlock Holmes or Mr. Magoo.

1. How many eyes are there on a one dollar bill?

2. Name the colors on a 7-11 sign.

3. Was Marilyn Monroe's beauty mark on the right or left side of her face?

4. Which hand does the Statue of Liberty use to hold her torch?

5. Which color stripe is on top of the American flag- red or white?

6. What shape is hidden in the Fed Ex logo?

7. What design can be seen on Oreo cookies?

8. What two numbers do not have letters on the telephone keypad?

9. In a deck of cards, what's unique about the King of Hearts?

10. Which side does Mr. Peanut wear his monocle on?

I Spy (Answers)

1. Four (Two on George Washington, one on the pyramid and one on the eagle)

2. Green, white, orange and red

3. Left

4. Right

5. Red

6. An arrow

7. 12 flowers, each with four petals, on each side

8. 1 and 0

9. He's the only king in the deck without a mustache.

10. His right side

Classic Conundrums

What gets whiter the dirtier it gets?

A chalkboard

VACATION VEXER

Anthony and Judy Salerno owned a pizzeria in the suburbs of Chicago. Years of hard work had enabled them to save up enough for the trip of a lifetime to see their long lost relatives who lived on the waters of Venice. At the same time, the couple had a tremendous fear of flying and boating there was out of the question. They finally settled on an acceptable means of transportation. What was it?

□   □   □

DAREDIVER

Elvin was an Olympic-caliber swimmer, known for his trick diving skills. Blindfolded, he leaped from a springboard into a 10-foot deep pool and didn't get wet. How did he manage this?

□   □   □

PAINT IT BLACK

A man dressed entirely in black is wearing a black mask covering his whole face. He stands at a crossroads in Blackville, a ghost of a town made up entirely of charcoal grey, run-down buildings. All of the streetlights are broken. There is no moon. A black-painted car without headlights drives straight toward him, but swerves in time and doesn't hit him. How did the driver avoid a collision?

VACATION VEXER (ANSWER)
To take either a car or train to Venice, Florida

DAREDIVER (ANSWER)
The pool was empty.

PAINT IT BLACK (ANSWER)
It's daytime.

PHRASE CRAZE

HOROBOD

(Robin Hood)

LITTLE LITTLE
LATE LATE

(Too little, too late)

BITING THE BULLET AT THE BAR

A priest, a minister and a rabbi walk into a bar and sit down at a table- but this riddle is not about them. It's about the little guy who comes in about five minutes later and asks the bartender for a glass of water. The bartender scowls, pulls out a double-barreled shotgun, points it at the little man and then lays it on the bar. The man thanks him and leaves, quite pleased. What just happened here?

☐   ☐   ☐

A JENNY-CRAIG STORY

Jenny and Craig hadn't seen each other for years when they met at a class reunion. Craig ribbed his former classmate, "Geez, Jenny. You must have put on a hundred pounds!" Jenny laughed, even though Craig was correct- and even though she wasn't overweight. What's the story here?

☐   ☐   ☐

HOSPITAL FOR THE HEALTHY

Waldo spent a couple of days in the hospital even though he wasn't sick or injured. In fact, physically there was absolutely nothing wrong with him, yet when it came time for him to leave, it was necessary for Waldo to be carried out. How come?

BITING THE BULLET AT THE BAR (ANSWER)
The man had a bad case of hiccups, which the bartender heard when he spoke. Instead of the water, the bartender decided to scare him by pulling out the gun. It worked like a charm and the man went away, cured.

A JENNY-CRAIG STORY (ANSWER)
It was a kindergarten reunion.

HOSPITAL FOR THE HEALTHY (ANSWER)
Waldo was a two-day old baby.

Classic Conundrums

What has to be broken before it can be used?

An egg

WEIGHTY BUSINESS

The economy is so slow that you find yourself working for your cousin in Jersey, affectionately known to one and all as "Tony The Torpedo".

Now, you are not at liberty to disclose the exact nature of your work, but let's just say that it involves mixing cement to keep things properly anchored in Raritan Bay.

One day, you are faced with a significant difficulty. You find yourself needing to mix exactly five gallons of water for enough cement for a pair of extra large overshoes. You have plenty of water, but you only have a 4-gallon and a 7-gallon bucket. They're not marked off, so you can't measure how much is in them. Now I ask you- are these bucket manufacturers showing the proper respect for their customers? I think not. Perhaps Cousin Tony should pay them a visit sometime.

But I digress. Back to the water problem. You recall we had one, er, "client" that had kicked the bucket, and two buckets that were the wrong size. Now how are we gonna do this job properly and leave the vicinity before some officers of the law show up and get the erroneous idea that we are somehow polluting the bay?

WEIGHTY BUSINESS (ANSWER)

Fill the 4-gallon bucket and dump it into the empty 7-gallon bucket. Fill the 4-gallon bucket again and dump it into the 7-gallon bucket until it is full. Now you have 1 gallon in the 4-gallon bucket. Empty the 7-gallon bucket and transfer the 1 gallon from the 4-gallon bucket into it. Now fill the 4-gallon bucket and pour it into the 7-gallon bucket and you have 5 gallons. Mix your quick-setting cement, turn your project over to the guys on the boat and make yourself scarce.

Rhyme Time

Until I am measured
I am not known.
Yet how you miss me
When I have flown.
What am I?

Time

CLUELESS

Disregarding any clues, you should be able to find below the only word in the English language that has four consecutive double letters.

SAUBNBOYOKCKLEUEEPSER

If you've gotten the drift, there's no need for further help here to find the only word with five consecutive vowels.

FUQRUETUHEERHIENLPG

Let's remove any doubt at this point. We think you know what's going on, so you should be able to find the longest word with only one vowel.

ASNTRYDENOGTUBHST

There are five words in the English language that have no rhyming equivalent. Depth and month are two of them. The other three are colors. Setting aside silver and purple, can you find the other color here?

SOILVRERANANDPGURPELE

CLUELESS (ANSWER)
If you deleted the words "any clues" as suggested,
you'd be left with **subbookkeeper**.

Continuing with that premise, you didn't need
"further help", so once those words were removed,
queueing was left as the solution.

The longest word with only one vowel, **strengths**,
became evident with the removal of "any doubt."

Finally, setting aside "silver and purple" yielded the
only other color that rhymes with no other
words - **orange**.

— PHRASE CRAZE —

T
E
G   **GO**

(Get up and go)

ALLWORLD

(It's a small world after all)

TRUMP TEASER

You might be thinking that even here, in *The Bathroom Brain Teasers Book*, The Donald gets his name in headlines. But this time it's his son making the news.

What you are about to read is truly amazing- or is it? Donald Trump Jr. was born in 1977. At some point during this decade, he will be able to say, "My father may lay claim to having his name spread all over creation, but I'm here today to tell you that I am one of very few people who can make this claim- I, Donald Trump Jr., was 37 years old two days ago. Next year, I will be 40."

How can The Donald's son accurately make that claim?

❏   ❏   ❏

PICTURE PURCHASE

An art aficionado bought a useless painting at a garage sale, but knew that he was getting a lot more than he paid for. How so?

TRUMP TEASER (ANSWER)
He, or anyone else who's born on December 31, can fashion such a statement. In Junior's case, he was born December 31, 1977. He can make that claim on January 1, 2016.

PICTURE PURCHASE (ANSWER)
The frame around it was invaluable.

Rhyme Time

Heart of Darkness,
Coat of Grain,
I was once alive,
Now feel no pain.
I never walk, but
Leave a Trail,
Circle head and pointed tail.
I grow shorter as the day goes on,
My waistline is a hexagon.
What am I?

A pencil

FORWARD THINKING

If we were across the pond and using the King's English, we might call this the 2,000 pound question. In the U.S.A. it would be, well, the 2,000 pound question.

Forward I'm heavy, backward I'm not. What am I?

LETTER PERFECT

Which of the following letter designs does not belong with the other six?

Y E N F A H Z

TURNING BACK THE HANDS OF TIME

The summer solstice occurs in late June. Do you know the longest day of the year?

FORWARD THINKING (ANSWER)
Ton

LETTER PERFECT (ANSWER)
The letter E, which requires four perfectly straight lines- All the others have three.

TURNING BACK THE HANDS OF TIME (ANSWER)
The headline to this teaser provided you a clue. The longest day of the year is when the clocks get turned back, generally the first Sunday of November, creating a 25-hour day.

Classic Conundrums

How many bricks does it take to complete a building made of brick?

Just one- The last one.

TOM SWIFTIES

The adverb makes the pun here. Example- "I won't use that electric saw again- it's too dangerous," Tom said **offhandedly**. "See how many of the following Tom Swifties you can fill in," we say **blankly.**

1. "You have the right to remain silent," Tom said
   _____.

2. "I just struck oil," Tom _____.

3. "I'm going to wear a ribbon around my arm," Tom said with _____.

4. "I've gone and dropped my toothpaste," said Tom
   _____.

5. "I came in through the main door," said Tom
   _____.

6. "On the beach, the only thing you can count on is the sea spray," Tom said _____.

7. "I really enjoy condiments made with chopped up pickles," Tom said with _____.

8. "I've heard that the Octomom wants more children," Tom said _____.

9. "It turns out that for all his money Donald actually WANTS his hair like that," Tom _____.

10. "I admit that I always have trouble being on time," Tom said _____.

Tom Swifties (Answers)

1. arrestingly

2. gushed

3. abandon

4. crestfallen

5. entranced

6. mistrustfully

7. relish

8. kiddingly

9. trumpeted

10. belatedly

PHRASE CRAZE

O _ ER _ T _ O _

(Painless operation)

SYMPHON

(Unfinished symphony)

MARQUEE MANGLERS

What's in a name? Plenty if you want to have a hit movie. Turn up your mental wattage or grab a thesaurus to decode the titles of these famous films.

1. "Apodictic Mettle"

2. "West Indian Picaroons"

3. "The Male Monarch's Linguistic Communication"

4. "The Veisalgia"

5. "Say Chap, What's the 20 on My Beater?"

6. "Vaqueros plus Extra-Terrestrials"

7. "Suggestions to Make One's Draconic Orientalis Proficient with Specialized Instruction and Practice"

8. "Arachnid Homo Sapien"

9. "The Terminal Atmospheric Topography Manipulator"

10. "Insomnious in the Emerald City"

MARQUEE MANGLERS (ANSWERS)

1. *True Grit*

2. *Pirates of the Caribbean*

3. *The King's Speech*

4. *The Hangover*

5. *Dude, Where's My Car?*

6. *Cowboys and Aliens*

7. *How To Train Your Dragon*

8. *Spider-man*

9. *The Last Airbender*

10. *Sleepless in Seattle*

PHRASE CRAZE

UALLS
NOW

(*All between us is over now*)

10SNE1

(*Tennis, anyone?*)

MINUTE MYSTERY

Psychic detectives Vaughn and Russ decided to take a
break from their heavy caseload to tour some of the
local points of interest. Russ wanted to go to the
Creaksonium, a creepy old building that seemed to
house the world's largest collection of cobwebs.

Russ was intent on the ancient exhibits while Vaughn
directed his attention at the pretty tour guide. It
occurred to Russ that things hadn't changed much
since they went on school trips together.

Vaughn was about to make his move when there came
a scream from upstairs, followed by a slam and a
muffled thud.

Charging up the nearby stairwell to investigate,
Vaughn and Russ found a closed door with a suicide
note pinned to it. Vaughn opened the door outward
and narrowly missed falling three stories into a
construction pit. The door had once led to an adjoining
building that had been demolished. It now opened only
on thin air, which Vaughn's feet beat frantically in vain
to find a landing.

As Russ helped pull his partner back in, Vaughn
announced to the group- with a quick wink at the tour
guide- that this was not suicide. It was indeed, murder
most foul.

How did Vaughn know?

MINUTE MYSTERY (ANSWER)
To slam a door which opened outward, the victim would have needed someplace to stand. Therefore, he was pushed and the murderer slammed the door.

❑   ❑   ❑

TRIVIAL TWOFERS

Here, you have two cracks at the same answer- If you can answer the trivia question, you also have the solution to the numerical teaser below it. Conversely, if you can figure out the sequentially proper number to fill in the blank, you've got the trivia question answered, too.

1. How many dominoes are in a standard set?
   43, 38, 34, 31, 29, __

2. What's the maximum amount of years that a U.S. president may be in office?
   2, 3, __, 12, 13, 20

3. What's the weight, in pounds, of a men's "shot" in the shot put?
   2, 4, __, 256, 65,536, 4,294,967,296

4. What's the only number with its letters in reverse alphabetical order?
   _, 11, 21, 31, 21, 11, 1

5. How many flavors of ice cream are in that famous Baskin-Robbins slogan?
   J 31, F 28, M __, A 30, M 31, J 30

6. How many nephews does Popeye have?
   T, N, E, S, S, F, _, T, T, O

7. In a perfect game in baseball, how many batters does a pitcher face?
   3, 9, __, 51, 153, 459

8. How many states in the U.S. begin with the letter "M"?
   S6, M6, T7, W9, T_, F6, S8

9. In the British game of draughts, each player starts out with how many pieces?
   1,440, 288, 72, 24, 12, __

10. How many feet tall is the Statue of Liberty?
    861, 458, 614, 586, ___

TRIVIAL TWOFERS (ANSWERS)

1. 28- Numbers are subtracted sequentially: 43 – 5, 38 – 4, etc.

2. 10- This is "T," as in tricky, on both counts. The number 10 is arrived at in the numerical sequence by counting numbers that begin with the letter "t"- two, three, ten... Regarding the answer to the trivia item, according to the 22nd Amendment to the Constitution, this maximum would be reached by a president completing two years of the term of his/her predecessor, then being elected to two full terms.

3. 16- The numbers are squared: 2 x 2 = 4, 4 x 4 = 16, etc.

4. 1- The numbers are a palindrome- they read the same forward and backward.

5. 31- Starting with January, the letters designate the months of the year and the numbers are the amount of days in that month.

6. 4- Pipeye, Peepeye, Pupeye, and Poopeye... The letters represent the first letter of numbers in the countdown from 10 to 1.

7. 27- The numbers are in sequential multiplications of 3: 3 x 3 = 9 x 3 = 27, etc.

8. 8- Maine, Maryland, Massachusetts, Michigan, Minnesota, Mississippi, Missouri, and Montana...The numbers correspond to the amount of letters in each day of the week: S (for Sunday) 6; M (for Monday) 6; etc.

9. 12- In the U.S., the game is known as checkers... The numerical solution is arrived at by divisions of 5, 4, 3, 2 and then 1 (1,440 ÷ 5 = 288 ÷ 4 = 72 ÷ 3 = 24 ÷ 2 = 12 ÷ 1 = 12).

10. 145- 148 feet if she's in heels! ...145 represents the last three digits of 86145, the pattern that is repeated in groups of three.

VOWEL PLAY

Following are some unique observations- words to live by, and words completed by simply filling in the vowels where applicable.

1.   'm nbdy, nbdy s prfct, nd thrfr 'm prfct.

2.   Yr ftr dpnds n yr drms, s g t slp!

3.   Bttr t rmn slnt nd b thght fl, thn t spk nd rmv ll dbt.

4.   f clttrd dsk s sgn f clttrd mnd, thn n mpty dsk...

5.   Clbcy sn't hrdtry.

6.   'v gt t st dwn nd wrk t whr stnd.

7.   Whr thr's wll, wnt t b n t.

8.   wst s trrbl thng t mnd.

9.   Ppl wh snr lwys fll slp frst.

10. Th tm t nsr tht th tlt wrks s bfr y rlly nd t.

VOWEL PLAY (ANSWERS)

1. I'm a nobody, nobody is perfect, and there fore I'm perfect.

2. Your future depends on your dreams, so go to sleep!

3. Better to remain silent and be thought a fool, than to speak and remove all doubt.

4. If a cluttered desk is a sign of a cluttered mind, then an empty desk…(is a sign of an empty mind.)

5. Celibacy isn't hereditary.

6. I've got to sit down and work out where I stand.

7. Where there's a will, I want to be in it.

8. A waist is a terrible thing to mind.

9. People who snore always fall asleep first.

10. The time to ensure that the toilet works is before you really need it.

Classic Conundrums

What was the name of the President of the United States in 2000?

His name was the same as it is now- Barack Obama.

INITIALLY SPEAKING

The following represent common lyrics, phrases, conversions and quotes. Crank up your gray matter and see how many you can grind out.

Example: 99= B. of B. on the W. (99 Bottles of Beer on the Wall)

1. 76= T. in the H. P.

2. 3= D. in an A. C.

3. 8= P. in the S. S.

4. 30= D. has S., A., J. and N.

5. 206= B. in the H. B.

6. 13= a B. D.

7. 5,280= F. in a M.

8. 50= W. to L. Y. L.

9. 9= P. on a B. T.

10. 87= F. S. and S. (Y. A. ...)

Initially Speaking (Answers)

1. 76 Trombones in the Hit Parade

2. 3 Digits in an Area Code

3. 8 Planets in the Solar System

4. 30 Days has September, April, June and November

5. 206 Bones in the Human Body

6. 13 equals a Baker's Dozen

7. 5,280 Feet in a Mile

8. 50 Ways to Leave Your Lover

9. 9 Players on a Baseball Team

10. 87 equals Four Score and Seven (Years Ago…)

Phrase Craze

FAREDCE

(Red in the face)

BA BS
0

(Two degrees above zero)

Touching Base

tI saw no enuJ 32, 3691, ta eht oloP sdnuorG nehw
ynaz steM redleifretnec ymmiJ llasreiP tfel sih tsom
elbaromem noisserpmi no weN kroY. llasreiP dah a
71-raey gib eugael reerac dekram yb eno lufroloc
tnedicni retfa rehtona. eH ecno deppets pu ot eht etalp
gniraew a seltaeB giw elihw gniyalp "ria ratiug" no sih
tab, del sreehc rof flesmih ni eht dleiftuo gnirud skaerb
ni yalp, dna dih dniheb eht stnemunom ta eht dlo
eeknaY muidatS dna "deklat" ot ebaB htuR. tuB sih
erutangis emag emac no taht enuJ noonretfa, eht
renepo fo a redaehelbuod tsniaga eht aihpledalihP
seillihP. weN s'kroY lraC yelliW dehctip a tnaillirb 0-5
tuotuhs; revewoh llasreiP saw eht klat fo eht nwot, ton
os hcum rof sih enotselim remoh, tub rof tahw eh did
ot etaromemmoc ti. gnicaF aihpledalihP rehctip sallaD
neerG, llasreiP detfol a pop ylf revo eht thgir-dleif ecnef
rof eht ht001 emoh nur fo sih reerac. tahW dewollof,
emos deredisnoc ot eb suoiralih. srehtO deredisnoc ti
enasni. eugaeL slaiciffo erew ton desuma. A yad retal,
a gnilur saw deussi ot tibihorp siht dnik fo roivaheb. fI
ev'uoy daer siht raf, uoy nac ylbaborp sseug tahw ti saw
taht llasreiP did ot etarbelec eht noisacco. t'naC uoy?

TOUCHING BASE (ANSWER)
He ran the bases backwards!

□   □   □

THE LEGEND OF BIZARRO

Bizarro, the masked avenger, fought for justice against
the evil rulers of his province. He would ride by night
to free those who had been wrongly imprisoned and
harass the bumbling soldiers of the evil General
Disarray by the dark of the moon.

Bizarro's escapades went on for years. He was beloved
by the villagers and despised by the authorities,
especially General Disarray.

Then one black night, it happened. Bizarro had
managed to waylay the armed vehicle which was
transporting brutally collected taxes to the capital.
He was making his way back to return the money to
the peasants, but was ambushed in the process. Even
Bizarro's legendary sword skills were not enough to
escape the trap set by General Disarray and his army.

Classic Conundrums

How many times can you subtract 2 from 22?

Only once, because then it's 20.

Bizarro was dragged off in chains and thrown in the stockade. In the morning at his trial, General Disarray found him guilty and sentenced him to a firing squad the next day at noon.

"Ha! Your firing squad does not frighten me, Disarray," Bizarro chided. "They are your soldiers and relatives and cannot hit a thing they aim at."

"I am glad that you accept your punishment, Bizarro," grinned the General through clenched teeth. "I'll tell you what- I will expand the squad's number to 100, have them stand but 20 feet from you, and I'll allow them to fire multiple times. Are you frightened now?"

"Ha! You fear Bizarro this much?" Bizarro taunted.

Now seething at the public humiliation, the General decided to play along. "My friend, you misunderstand. Let it not be said that I am not a compassionate man. If you feel that I'm being unfair, you may have a hand in arranging your own execution. It will be your honor to assemble the men and arrange them as you like. As long as you stay tied to the post at the center of the field and they are no more than 20 feet away, their formation is yours to command. And to show how generous I can be, if you are still alive by one half hour past high noon, you will be released."

How did Bizarro arrange the firing squad so that they had to cut him loose at 12:30?

THE LEGEND OF BIZARRO (ANSWER)

He placed them in a circle around him. They were 20 feet away and he was still tied to the post, but the soldiers were afraid to start firing. They knew that they were lousy shots and would probably just miss and hit the other squad members. None of them took a shot and, as per the General's sentence, Bizarro was set free.

Rhyme Time

I'll never be seen, no matter how bold.
You can capture me, but don't try to hold.
I have no throat and can't say a word,
But when I'm around I can often be heard.
What am I?

The Wind

GO FIGURE

1. The numbers below correlate with the words in this sentence. What's the missing number?
   3 7 5 9 4 ? 5 2 4 8

2. Divide 30 by half and add ten. What's the answer?

3. Which of the following isn't as "perfect" as the others?
   a) 1   b) 4   c) 7   d) 9

4. Ralph has eight boys and each one has a sister. In all, how many kids does Ralph have?

5. Oddly enough, we think you might be able to provide the missing letter in the following sequence.
   O, T, F, S, _, E, T

6. What is the only case where half of 5 is 4?

7. Willie has twice as many brothers as he has sisters. His sister Wanda has five times as many brothers as she has sisters. How many brothers and sisters are there in the family?

8. The following Roman numeral equation, translated to 11 plus 1 equals 10, is obviously wrong. How can you correct it without changing it? X I + I = X

9. Oscar and Wally were playing tennis on their club's only clay court. After five sets, they each won three. How is this possible?

10. Multiply 11,111,111 by itself and what do you get?

Go Figure (Answers)

1. 3- The numbers equal the amount of letters in each word of the sentence.

2. 70

3. C- The others are perfect squares.

4. 9

5. N- for the number nine… In ascending order beginning with "One," these are the first letters of odd numbers.

6. Half of FIVE is "IV", in Roman numerals.

7. There are 5 boys and 2 girls.

8. Simply turn it upside down and it reads X = I + IX.

9. They were doubles partners and defeated their opponents 3 sets to 2.

10. 12345678987654321!

Classic Conundrums

What has a foot at each end and one in the middle?

A yardstick

ON A VERY SPECIAL EPISODE OF SURVIVOR ISLAND...

Contestants on the reality show *Survivor Island* were in a fix. Supplies were running dangerously low and most of the island was overrun with man-eating crabs. They needed to get across the shark-infested lagoon to a neighboring island with fresh stocks and an anti-crab electric fence. The problem was that Jack weighed 200 pounds, Mike weighed 140 pounds and Lori tipped the scales at exactly 100 pounds. The weight limit for their tiny dugout canoe was 250 pounds, so there was no way they could all fit.

Knowing that the crabs would be there by sundown, how did all three avoid starvation and/or becoming crab bait?

□   □   □

TENNIS ELBOW

Is there a better than 50-50 chance that the next men's U.S. Open tennis champion will have more than the average number of elbows?

ON A VERY SPECIAL EPISODE OF SURVIVOR ISLAND... (ANSWER)

Mike and Lori took the canoe to the new island. Lori stayed at the new campsite while Mike paddled back. When he arrived, he turned the canoe over to Jack, who beat a hasty retreat to the new crab-proof beach. Jack landed the boat with a thump, and as he climbed ashore, Lori got back in the canoe to go pick up Mike. That night, with full bellies, they slept the sleep of the crabless.

TENNIS ELBOW (ANSWER)

Yes- Since the average number of elbows on a human is slightly less than two, anyone with two elbows has more than the average.

□   □   □

RUNNING NUMBERS

In what order are the numbers below?
8 5 4 9 1 7 6 3 2 0

Classic Conundrums

What goes up and never comes down?

Your age

BACK AND FORTH

Without switching their order, how can you make these numbers read like a palindrome- the same from left to right as right to left?   14351026987

❑   ❑   ❑

WORDS TO LIVE BY

Once again, you're asked to replace the missing vowels to reveal the words of wisdom.

1. Th rly brd mght gt th wrm, bt th scnd ms gts th chs.

2. lwys brrw mny frm pssmst. H wn't xpct t bck.

3. Knwldg s knwng tmt s frt; Wsdm s nt pttng t n frt sld.

4. Y d nt nd prcht t skydv. Y nly nd prcht t skydv twc.

5. nmplymnt sn't wrkng.

6. Lgt trvls fstr thn snd. Ths s why sm ppl ppr brght ntl y hr thm spk.

7. Th sl prps f chld's mddl nm s s h cn tll whn h's rlly n trbl.

8. Hlf f th ppl n th wrld r blw vrg.

9. Nvr ht mn wth glsss. Ht hm wth bsbll bt.

10. Prctc mks prfct, bt nbdy's prfct, s why prctc?

Running Numbers (Answer)
Alphabetical order

Back and Forth (Answer)
Make them Roman Numerals- I IV III V X II VI IX VIII VII

Words to Live By (Answers)

1. The early bird might get the worm, but the second mouse gets the cheese.

2. Always borrow money from a pessimist. He won't expect it back.

3. Knowledge is knowing a tomato is a fruit; Wisdom is not putting it in a fruit salad.

4. You do not need a parachute to skydive. You only need a parachute to skydive twice.

5. Unemployment isn't working.

6. Light travels faster than sound. This is why some people appear bright until you hear them speak.

7. The sole purpose of a child's middle name is so he can tell when he's really in trouble.

8. Half of the people in the world are below average.

9. Never hit a man with glasses. Hit him with a baseball bat.

10. Practice makes perfect, but nobody's perfect, so why practice?

SINGING A SONG FOR SIXPENCE

Warren Smorgasbord, the fabulously wealthy but socially conscious entrepreneur, found himself sitting next to a scruffily dressed beach bum type at a Tiki bar in Honolulu. The two struck up a conversation and Smorgasbord asked the man what he did for a living. The man claimed that he had a unique talent. He knew every song ever written, and if you gave him a lady's name, he would sing you an actual song with that name in it. He guaranteed that the song would be verifiable no matter how long the name.

"Well, I'm a betting man," said Smorgasbord. "Tell you what. I'll bet whatever's in my wallet against one of those flaming Rum Wiki Wacky Waikiki drinks that I can give you a name that you can't come up with a song for. In fact, it's my daughter's- Maria Kathryn Elizabeth Ethel Conchata, Evelyn Rebecca Suzette Smorgasbord-Von Hindenbacker."

Quite a challenge on the surface, but the beach bum went home with a well-stuffed wallet and Smorgasbord went home several thousand dollars wiser.

How did the beachcomber win the bet?

SINGING A SONG FOR SIXPENCE (ANSWER)
He simply sang *Happy Birthday* with the young lady's name in it.

□   □   □

DRIVER'S TEST

Egbert lives in Maine. Over the next few days, he drives to Virginia and then home to Maine. The entire time, Egbert was driving in a northbound lane. How come?

□   □   □

TABLE TALK

You put it on the table, cut it and then properly pass portions of it around the table, but you never eat it. What is it?

Classic Conundrums

The more you have, the less you see. What is it?

ssǝuʞɹɐᗡ

PIRATE PROMOTION

Infamous pirate Stinky Pete, the terror of the Spanish Main, was in need of a new second-in-command. His previous one had left to serve on a naval disciplinary board. In other words, he had walked the plank.

Seniority meant nothing to the captain. He wanted his smartest crewmember backing him up, so he devised a devious test.

Calling the crew to the main deck, he produced five bandannas- two red and three white, and showed them to the three top candidates who were lined up face to back. They were then fitted with two eye patches each. Next, the captain tied a bandanna high on each man's head, above where he could possibly see it, and put the other two bandannas away.

His face seized by a devilish grin, Stinky Pete ordered the eye patches removed.

Now the third sailor in line could see the first two, the second could see the bandanna on the first and the first sailor could see neither his own bandanna nor the others.

"Arrghh, any one of ye may speak first and guess your bandanna color. If ye be correct, ye be my new first mate. If ye be wrong, by Poseidon's beard, I'll have ye thrown to the sharks!"

There were a few tense minutes of silence, but then the first in line spoke up and said, "My bandanna is white."

Did he get the promotion or was he thrown to the sharks?

DRIVER'S TEST (ANSWER)
Egbert may live in Maine, but he started this trip well south of Virginia, traveled northbound through the state and then home.

TABLE TALK (ANSWER)
A deck of cards

PIRATE PROMOTION (ANSWER)
He got the promotion. He figured it thus:
The third sailor was silent. That meant that the first two weren't wearing red, because if they were, he would have known his was white. The only possibilities were white-white and red-white.

The second sailor deduced this but didn't guess, because seeing the first sailor's bandanna didn't give him the answer.

The first sailor, who saw no bandannas, figured from the lack of response from the second that his had to be white, since the third saw either white-white or red-white. Had the second sailor seen red, he'd have known that his was white and would have answered.

Shiver me timbers!

Classic Conundrums
What can run but never walks, has a mouth but never talks, a head but never weeps, and a bed but never sleeps?

A river

BASEBALL BAFFLER

Step up to the plate and see if you can handle this hardball teaser that actually occurred.

Nolan Ryan... Bob Feller... Justin Verlander... Give them their due with their 100 mph heaters, but they couldn't hold a candle to the flame-throwing of Hayden Siddhartha "Sidd" Finch according to *Sports Illustrated's* April 1, 1985 cover story.

The magazine reported that the 28-year-old eccentric rookie from Tibet had been blowing away the Mets coaching staff during spring training with far and away the fastest fastball anyone had ever seen- an amazing 168 miles per hour.

So why was it, then, that Finch's name made an equally quick disappearance from the sports pages?

□   □   □

A FAMILIAR FACE

Cornelius was vacationing at Disney World when he ran into his long lost uncle. He disappeared from the family before Cornelius was even born. Cornelius had never met nor even seen him, not even in a picture. Nonetheless, Cornelius easily recognized his uncle. How come?

BASEBALL BAFFLER (ANSWER)
Note the date of the issue, April 1- It was an April Fool's joke by the publication.

A FAMILIAR FACE (ANSWER)
Cornelius' uncle was his dad's identical twin.

☐   ☐   ☐

HORSEPLAY

1. A man riding on horseback left from New York for San Francisco on Tuesday and arrived on the very same Tuesday. How can this be?

2. A horse is tied to a 15-foot rope and a bale of hay is 25 feet away. How is it that the horse is able to eat that hay?

Classic Conundrums

What is it that you break just by saying its name?

Silence

What I "Ment" To Say Was...

"Ment" is the common element in this assortment. Use your judgment to reach enlightenment. We would like to offer you encouragement as we bring puzzlement and amusement to your assessment of the assignment.

1. Often found on e-mails and vacuum cleaners. What I "ment" to say was...

2. Under the floor. What I "ment" to say was...

3. Adding it on. What I "ment" to say was...

4. Putting off. What I "ment" to say was...

5. Often found on blisters. What I "ment" to say was...

6. Go along to get along. What I "ment" to say was...

7. Hit the road Jack and don't you come back no more. What I "ment" to say was...

8. All right Jack, you can come back and it's business as usual. What I "ment" to say was...

9. They do it to concentrate fissionable uranium. What I "ment" to say was...

10. Unexpected difficulty in coming up with the last one for the quiz. What I "ment" to say was...

HORSEPLAY (ANSWER)

1. The horse's name was Tuesday.
2. He simply walks over and eats it. The horse may be tied to the rope, but the rope isn't tied to anything!

WHAT I "MENT" TO SAY WAS... (ANSWERS)

1. attachment

2. basement

3. supplement

4. postponement

5. ointment

6. appeasement

7. banishment

8. reinstatement

9. enrichment

10. predicament

Classic Conundrums

What's greater than God, more evil than the devil, the poor have it, the rich need it, and if you eat it, you die?

Nothing

PACKING POODLES

You're leaving for your oceanfront mansion to summer in the Hamptons. Of course you want to take your precious little pets along, but you find that if you put one poodle per pet carrier, you are one carrier short. If you double up and put two poodles in each carrier, you find that you have a carrier left over. How many poodles and how many carriers do you have?

❑   ❑   ❑

SPRINGTIME SIBLINGS

Billy's mom has three kids. One is named April and the other is named May. What is the name of the third child?

❑   ❑   ❑

BIRTHDAY BLUES

Barney Jones was born before the turn of the century—the twentieth century. The odd thing about Barney's initial celebration is that he was eight years old on his first birthday. How can that be?

PACKING POODLES (ANSWER)
You have 4 poodles and 3 carriers. Tell Jeeves to run an errand to the pet shop and then have James bring the car around.

SPRINGTIME SIBLINGS (ANSWER)
Billy

BIRTHDAY BLUES (ANSWER)
Barney was born February 29, 1896. The first leap year after he was born occurred in 1904, as there was no leap year in 1900 (only centuries divisible by 400 are leap years).

PHRASE CRAZE

DEATH LIFE
(Life after death)

NEPAINCK
(Pain in the neck)

UMADESA
(Made in the USA)

THE BRIDGE ON THE RIVER SPY

The time: World War II

The place: The border between Switzerland and Germany

Sgt. Schultz, the new guard in the tower, was given strict orders not to let anyone cross the bridge between the two countries. He was to send anyone coming from the Swiss side back to their own nation. If he caught anyone coming from the German side, they were to be shot.

Schultz, who had just been given this plum assignment because of the great work he did at a local Stalag, wanted to be conscientious. He checked the bridge every three minutes because he knew that it would take at least six minutes to cross.

As it happened, there was a beautiful young Fraulein (Code Name: X-19) who needed to smuggle the Nazi air-defense plan to her contact in Switzerland. She had no papers and she knew that crossing the bridge to freedom was verboten.

She started walking across the bridge and Sgt. Schultz was right on time, yet she got into Switzerland with her secret papers. How'd she do it?

THE BRIDGE ON THE RIVER SPY (ANSWER)

She waited until Sgt. Schultz had just completed his rounds and went inside. Immediately after, she started crossing the bridge. At the three minute mark, she turned around and started walking back to Germany. At this point, Schultz came out and ordered her to stop and turn around. She was not allowed to cross the bridge into Germany and so "returned" to Switzerland, the country Schultz thought she had come from in the first place.

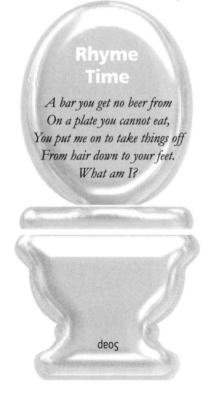

Rhyme Time

A bar you get no beer from
On a plate you cannot eat,
You put me on to take things off
From hair down to your feet.
What am I?

soap

CHIME TIME

A man arrived home late one night. When he opened the door, he heard the clock chime once. A half hour later, it chimed once. The same thing happened another half hour later. And a half hour after that, the clock yet again chimed only once. If the clock chimes the number of times to indicate the hour, and then once on the half-hour, what time did the man arrive home?

□   □   □

NAME THAT TUNE

The following couple of ditties "in and of themselves" are literal representations of song names. Test yourself to find out if you are sharp or flat...

1. VMEOORNLMIOGHNTT

2. TSHTERNANIGGEHRTS

CHIME TIME (ANSWER)

Midnight- He heard the last chime at twelve, one at 12:30, another at l:00 A.M. and one more at 1:30.

NAME THAT TUNE (ANSWER)

1. *Moonlight in Vermont*

2. *Strangers in the Night*

— **SIMPLE STUFF** —

How many outs are there in an inning?

Six

What does the Statue of Liberty stand for?

Because it can't sit down.

If a girl who works in a candy store is five-foot-two and wears a size five shoe, what does she weigh?

Candy

Classic Conundrums

How can you put your left hand in your right-hand pants pocket and your right hand in your left-hand pants pocket without crossing your hands?

Put your pants on backwards.

RAIDERS OF DOOM

Archaeologist Illinois Bones had just barely escaped from the bloodthirsty Ho-Ho-Vitos tribe who was hunting him for his snack cakes when he stumbled upon the fabled fork in the road. This was it, the place he had been searching for ever since the yellowed old treasure map had come into his possession.

As the legend foretold, the forks were paved with gold and led off into the dense jungle. At the end of one trail, he would find a thousand tons of pure gold, buckets of flawless diamonds, the secret to eternal life, the cure for all diseases and a free Netflix coupon.

At the end of the other trail, however, he would find a horrifying death in a pit of fire-breathing snakes.

Two burly guards stood at the trailhead of each route. Bones knew that according to legend, one guard always told the truth and the other always lied. He also knew that once he chose a path, there was no turning back, for he would surely be struck dead on the spot. The ancients had decreed that only one question may be asked to distinguish between these otherwise identical looking trails, but there was no way of telling the liar from the truth-teller and no do-overs were allowed.

Bones thought for a moment, scratching his well-scarred chin and squinting off into the distance. Finally he smiled and said to himself, "Fortune and glory, pal, fortune and glory", and then asked his question. How did Illinois know which trail to choose?

RAIDERS OF DOOM (ANSWER)

He said, "If I ask the other guard which trail leads to the treasure, which one would he tell me?" Once he had his answer, he took the opposite trail.

Rhyme Time

My top and my bottom are twins of a kind.
The middle of me makes one body combined.
I'm used to pass time and provide quite a thrill.
If I stand tall and still, run faster I will.
What am I?

An hourglass

OPPOSITES ATTRACT

Here are some common words scrambled with their opposites. Restore balance to the universe by rearranging these diametric duos into proper antonyms. There are two words in each scrambled set of letters.

Example: ocorrhip = rich/poor

1.   igrlhdkat

2.   hduylslni

3.   glouydon

4.   rtewdy

5.   wadmtlie

6.   ssttiflar

7.   dhonionmgtni

8.   vodeloig

9.   rlysaoctmer

10.   dpeimlutyvdili

OPPOSITES ATTRACT (ANSWERS)

1.   light/dark

2.   dull/shiny

3.   old/young

4.   wet/dry

5.   wild/tame

6.   first/last

7.   noon/midnight

8.   good/evil

9.   stormy/clear

10.   multiply/divide

PHRASE CRAZE

FUNNY FUNNY
WORDS WORDS
WORDS WORDS

(Too funny for words)

STA4NCE

(For instance)

ALIEN MIND CONTROL

On a hot, dry summer night in 1947, in the great American southwestern desert not far outside of Roswell, NM, a strange little man shuffled into a dimly lit cantina and took a seat at the bar.

"I am an alien," he announced. "I have taken human form to study your primitive culture. At first I found your society interesting, but now I have concluded that you are all weak-brained. If I wished to, I could control your feeble minds at will. Give me a beer."

"If you're an alien like you say, then you're not from around here, so let's see your money," drawled the proprietor, flicking a besotted gecko off some beer foam spilled on the bar.

"I have no money, but you will give me a beer," said the strange visitor, with a face barely visible outside the turned-up collar of his jacket.

"What are you gonna do? Use mind control?" The barkeep snorted derisively to the great amusement of the motley patrons who by now had taken notice.

"No, that would be unethical," replied the stranger. "Nevertheless, you will give me a beer."

"How are you gonna do that?", asked the bartender.

"If I merely demonstrate my mind control power, will you give me a beer?"

"Okay, I guess it's a slow night and we could use a little entertainment. Why not?", the proprietor volunteered.

"Very well...Then we have, as you earthlings say, 'a deal'. To demonstrate I shall do a card trick."

"No funny business with a marked deck or nuthin'," warned the bartender.

"Of course not. We shall use a deck of the mind, and through my great mental powers, I shall force everyone in here to choose the same card."

"Okay, go on with your trick," said the bartender.

"It is no trick, earthling. It is merely the power of my superior mind. Now for this mental deck we need some face cards. I want you to think of three people who you care for- parents, señoritas, friends...anyone important to you. Let these three faces rotate through your mind, paying equal attention to each as it rolls by. Round and round they go- keep concentrating, and the next face you see, I want you to.....stop! That is the face you have selected."

Classic Conundrums

What has no beginning, end or middle?

A doughnut

Whether they would have owned up to it or not, the cowpokes, ranchers and assorted riffraff were now intrigued, for they all had the image of someone they loved in their mind's eye.

"Now, puny-brained earthlings, count the number of letters in that name. As you chose this name from a field of three, multiply the number of letters by three and note the result."

The bartender wrote his number on a legal pad while his customers jotted theirs down on napkins or in the condensation on the outside of their beer glasses.

The mesmerizing stranger continued, "Now picture as face cards three people you loathe. A lover who jilted you, a boss, a bully in school… someone, anyone you really dislike. Let these three faces flash through your mind. Keep them going- keep them circling through your consciousness…now hold it, hold it- stop! That is the face you've chosen. Take the number of letters in this detested name and use it to multiply the number you wrote down earlier."

At this point, there was no other sound than the howl of a distant coyote. Old Bert sat at the end of the bar, furiously doing the calculation on an improvised abacus hastily assembled from beer nuts and bottle caps. "Finally, multiply that result by three," directed the alien. "Don't worry that your feeble, unevolved minds cannot keep up, for now I am directing them," the self-proclaimed alien hissed, barely above a whisper.

"You now have your final, unique number based on the people you have loved and hated in your lives."

The mysterious stranger paused a few moments to give everyone the chance to check their calculations.

"At this point we will return to the imaginary deck of cards. There are 13 cards per suit, ranging from the Ace, considered as 1, to the King, which is 13. If your number is 13 or less, you now know the value of your imaginary card. If, however, your number is greater than 13, you must add the digits of the number together. For example, 123 would be 1+2+3 = 6. Keep reducing your number until you have a number that is 13 or less. That is the value of your card."

Old Jed in the back corner was so confused, he rescued the worm from his tequila to ask it for help. Eventually, after using all his fingers and toes and whatever else was close at hand, he came up with his number.

"Now as to suit," the stranger said with a dramatic flourish, for he now knew that he held them in the palm of his hand- or tentacle, or whatever he had up his sleeve. "We will take them one at a time: Ace to 3 is hearts; 4 to 6, diamonds. If you have a card between 7 and 9, spades. Ten and face cards would be clubs."

There were a lot of sweating Stetsons in the bar, but everyone now had their card.

"I would like my beer now," the stranger said.

"I haven't seen any mind control yet," sneered the skeptical bartender.

"What was your card?", asked the stranger.

"Nine of spades," he answered.

"And what was your card?", the stranger challenged Bert.

"Nine o' spades."

Facing Old Jed he asked, "And yours?"

"Nine a' spades," Old Jed answered, now more confused than ever.

An astonished murmur swept across the bar as everyone revealed that their card, arrived at independently, was the nine of spades.

"So you see, dim-witted creatures, I have exercised mind control over you, forcing you all to pick the nine of spades."

With that, the bartender paid up and the alien knocked back his beer, walked through the swinging doors and off into the night, leaving the bartender to wonder. Was he rooked by a master or did he indeed play host to a beer-drinking alien?

What do you think? Did the alien force *you* to choose the same card as well?

ALIEN MIND CONTROL (EXPLANATION)
Why don't you just stop reading here? Why spoil the fun?

Alright, if you insist- Here's the spoiler:

Any number multiplied by 9 will yield a number which, when you add the digits repeatedly until you get a single number, will always come out to 9.
9 X 3= 27...2 + 7=9. 5 X 9 =45...4 + 5=9 and so on.

Nothing was multiplied by 9 here, but it was multiplied by 3 twice, which is the same as multiplying by 9 once. Once 9 is assured by the rules of the trick, spades will always be the suit.

PHRASE CRAZE

PWROOGRRESKS

(Work in progress)

poFISHnd

(A big fish in a little pond)

WHAT IS IT?

1. You can see me and you can feel me, but if you touch me, you will die.

2. You take away the outside and cook the inside. Then you eat the outside and throw away the inside.

3. I come at night without being called, and am lost in the day without being stolen.

4. I get bigger the more you take away from me.

5. Keep me whole and I can be anyone. Break me to pieces and I am no one.

6. The more I dry, the wetter I get.

7. I have a neck, but no head and two arms, but no hands.

8. I start with the letter E. I end with the letter E. I usually have only one letter, but I am not the letter E!

9. What seven-letter word becomes longer when you remove its third letter?

10. What's made by light and yet does not contain any light?

WHAT IS IT? (ANSWERS)

1.   The sun
2.   An ear of corn
3.   A star
4.   A hole
5.   A mirror
6.   A towel
7.   A shirt
8.   An envelope
9.   Lounger
10.   A shadow

Rhyme Time

I may fall, but I never break.
Children I may cause to quake.
You lose energy as I come your way.
I'm part of your week,
But not your day.
What am I?

Night

STATING THE FACTS

Ten statements follow below. How many in this quiz are true?

1.   There is one false statement.

2.   There are two false statements.

3.   There are three false statements.

4.   There are four false statements.

5.   There are five false statements.

6.   There are six false statements.

7.   There are seven false statements.

8.   There are eight false statements.

9.   There are nine false statements.

10.   There are ten false statements.

STATING THE FACTS (ANSWER)

Two- Number 9 is a true statement because 1 through 8 and 10 are false. The very first sentence of the quiz- "Ten statements follow below." –is also true.

SIMPLE STUFF

What's the greatest worldwide use of cowhide?

To cover cows

If King Kong went to Hong Kong to play ping-pong but fell on his bong bong and went bye-bye, what would they put on his coffin?

A lid

What is it that you sit on, sleep on and brush your teeth with?

A chair, a bed and a toothbrush

Classic Conundrums

In an all red, one-story house, what color are the stairs?

A one-story home doesn't have any stairs.

TRIVIQUATIONS

Fill in the missing numbers and solve the equations.

$$\frac{\text{London Olympics Year}}{\text{Mt. Rushmore Faces}} - \text{Spanish Steps in Italy} = \text{Steps at U.S. Capitol Building}$$

Stooges x Dalmatians – Musketeers = Bowling Perfection

$$\frac{\text{Fabled Road}} = \text{Continents} \times \frac{\text{Yogi Number}}{} + \frac{\text{Jackson \_\_\_}}{\text{"\_\_\_ Easy Pieces"}}$$

ANSWERS

$$\frac{2012}{4} - 138 = 365 \text{ (one for each day of the year)}$$

3 X 101 - 3 = 300

Route 66 = 7 X 8 + 5 + 5

SUDOKU PUZZLES

Fill in the grid so that every row, column and 3x3 box contains every number from 1 to 9 inclusively.

Bonus: Answer the Sudoku Stumper by filling in the open boxes suggested by the clues and you're on your way to solving the puzzle...Or solve the puzzle and you've solved the Stumper!

Easy

In what year did Joseph Gayetty invent toilet paper?
Sudoku clues: **E2, E3, E5, E6**

Moderate

How many bathrooms are there in the White House? 35
Sudoku clues: **C3, F6**

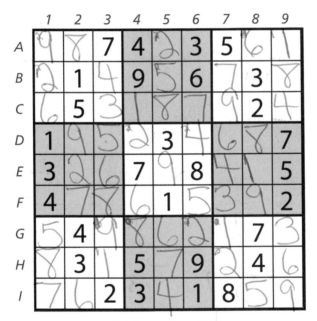

Solution on Page 108

Sudoku stems from the Japanese term 'su', meaning
"number" and 'doku', meaning "single."

Difficult

How many rolls of toilet paper, on average, are used in the Pentagon building daily?

Sudoku clues: **G2, C6, D9**

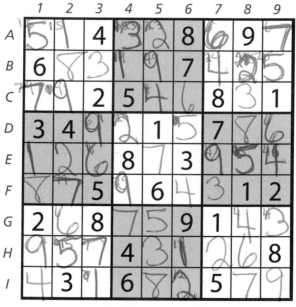

Solution on Page 109

*The numbers in a Sudoku
puzzle add up to 405.*

Expert

The longest Monopoly game played in a bathtub lasted how many hours?

Sudoku clues: **E1, A7**

Solution on Page 109

In Japan, Sudoku is called Number Place.

TUB TRIVIA

ACROSS

1 Relinquish
5 Ending with bed or home
10 Sprinted
14 GI miscreant
15 ___ du jour
16 ___ d'Orsay
17 M. Descartes
18 Siren
19 Sky bear
20 47 Across was one
23 Ampersands
24 Today
25 Bryant and Ekberg
28 Settled the bill
30 Machine part
33 Miss Burnett
34 "The Forsyte ___"
35 Singer Patti
36 Stabbed 47 Across
39 Country road phenomena
40 Dying vessels
41 Vex
42 Pierre's soul
43 A lot
44 More skillful
45 Shake up
46 Part of TLC
47 Was murdered in the bathtub
53 Newsman Roger
54 Reference work
55 Disorderly profusion
57 Exhort
58 Springe
59 Miss Ferber
60 Changed the color
61 City on the St. Lawrence
62 Abstruse

DOWN

1 Hatchback
2 Aquarian prop
3 Complete
4 They have their ups and downs
5 Ankle bone
6 Rock debris
7 Part of QED
8 Bell town of Italy
9 Fiendish
10 Tepee Mrs.
11 Sound of contentment
12 Child's play
13 Prefix with phragm
21 ___ sides (everywhere)
22 Drowse a bit
25 Ghana's capital
26 O.T. Book
27 Seeing red
28 Bit of candy
29 Gets on
30 USMA person
31 Whence sisal
32 Founder of Barnard C.
34 Steal the show
35 Chose
37 Cloverleaf element
38 Wozzeck, e.g.
43 Forefront
44 Lass
45 Blase
46 Mrs. Luce
47 Courtroom dozen
48 Periphery
49 ___ time (never)
50 Ending with cell
51 Staffer
52 ___ down (soften)
53 Mire
56 Broach

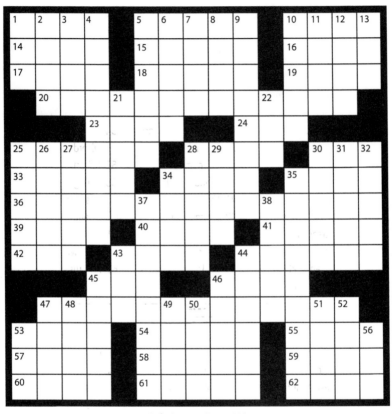

Solution on Page 110

"Men in their forties are like The New York Times
*Sunday crossword puzzle: tricky, complicated, and
you're never really sure you got the right answer."*
- Carrie, from the TV series Sex and the City

BATHROOM LAST AND FIRST

ACROSS

1,12 Across: Bathroom must
6 Subsequently
11 Ear-to-ear carpet
12 See 1 Across
14 Amble
15 Vine support
17 Jargon
18 Heroic stories
20 Part of IBM
21 Reo's maker
22 Blazing
23 Make over
24 Whodunit pioneer
25 Latitude
26 Scuba type
27 Knightly deeds
29 Rigorous
30 Poverty
31 Laudatory review
32 Amplified
35 "It" quality
39 Moslem VIP
40 Drive away
41 Mat. Time
42 Peruvian money
43 Transactions
44 Skin problem
45 ___ generis
46 Pronouncements
47 Sleuth Sam
48 Use a burin
50 See 52 Across
52, 50 Across: Inventor of 12 Across
53 Beat par on a hole
54 Youthful years
55 Charger

DOWN

1 He started it
2 Breathing apparatus
3 Able
4 Grasp
5 Kind of cattle
6 Duds
7 Compel
8 Standoffs
9 Pipe bend
10 Ease
11 Needleman
13 Very dry stuff
14 Gradient
16 Emporium
19 Shrill
22 Emoted
23 Cleft
25 Nasty look
26 Fiend
28 Alpaca's milieu
29 Band instruments
31 Substitutes
32 Old-hat
33 Sum
34 Glory in
35 Throne
36 Got away
37 Smoothed, as wood
38 Beef on the hoof
40 Niche
43 Lounge piece
44 Delicious or Rome
46 Mrs. Knight
47 Wise guy
49 Caviar
51 Squealer

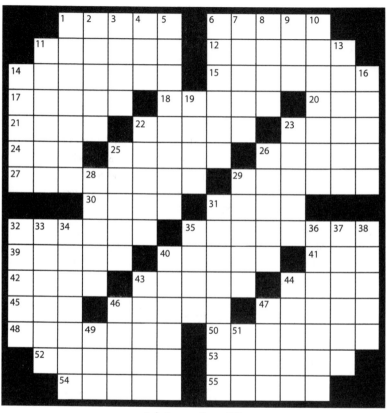

Solution on Page 110

A crossword puzzle creator is known as a cruciverbalist.

RUB A DUB DUB

ACROSS

1 African arroyo
5 Rampart slope
10 Jack's giant
14 Rubaiyat man
15 Henry VII or VII
16 Police crackdown
17 Miss Horne
18 Veldt beast
19 Bell sound
20 See 29 Across
22 Tight-fisted
24 Dolphin genus
25 Sound of distress
26 Leery

29, 20 Across:
Responsible for 38
Down in 1790
33 Merry
34 Vanished
35 Miss Turner
36 Get one's goat
37 VIPs of India
40 Grog base
41 Wave-borne
43 Track ____
44 Roly-poly
46 Bare
48 Pursued

49 Rough cross
50 Pillage
51 Destitute one
54 Liner's window
58 Mr. Guthrie
59 Gypsy card
61 Spruce
62 Regan's father
63 Void
64 Bankrupt
65 Breathe hard
66 Small change
67 Catcalls

DOWN

1 Eat voraciously
2 Part of USA
3 Charles or Bill
4 Khomeini's language
5 Phlegmatic
6 Vatican body
7 Tennis term
8 Carl Reiner's son
9 Inmate
10 First or nth
11 Accrual
12 Call up
13 Nervous
21 Does handwork

23 ____ Mahal
25 ____ - arms
26 Diva's soli
27 See 38 Down
28 Yardman, in autumn
29 Had in store
30 Paddock mamas
31 Busy
32 Dubbed
34 Avarice
38, 27 Down, 45 Down:
What 29 Across did in
1790
39 Not ____ (mediocre)

42 O'Hare or Dulles
45 See 38 Down
47 "Rue Morgue" author
48 Conquistador
50 At large
51 Feeler
52 Surroundings
53 ____ Bator
54 Nanny's vehicle
55 Whether ____
56 Liner's pool
57 Personalities
60 "Exodus" hero

Solution on Page 111

Comedian Jon Stewart, host of cable TV's The Daily Show, *proposed to his future wife through a personalized puzzle created with assistance from Will Shortz, the crossword editor of* The New York Times.

THE "FIRST" BATHROOM

ACROSS

1 Mrs. Truman
5 Goes a round
10 Yemeni
14 Proceedings
15 Unsaid
16 Prefix with medic
17, 35 Across: Said to be installed by 54 across
20 Achy feeling
21 Half
22 Yoohoo!
23 Went pellmell
24 Role for Olivier
28 Hustles
29 Disconsolate
32 Lend ____ (harken)
33 Blabbed
34 Decline
35 See 17 Across
38 Deceiver
39 Unchallenging
40 Misdid
41 Orch. offering
42 "Play it ____ lays"
43 Goodies
44 Flinders
45 Relative
46 Go along with
49 Got to
54 See 17 Across
56 Rel. of etc.
57 Family girl
58 Ballet movement
59 TV staple
60 Shirts
61 Beach feature

DOWN

1 Vespertilians
2 Iterate
3 Ending with pun or fun
4 Ump's call
5 "Sesame ____"
6 French economist
7 Impersonates
8 Costa
9 Panic
10 Plant pest
11 Stand OK
12 In ____ (programmed)
13 Infant
18 Be innate
19 Little piggies
23 Turbid
24 Greets
25 Hit musical
26 Tin or zinc
27 He played The Cowardly Lion
28 Lift up
29 Petrarch's beloved
30 Beginning
31 Plantains
33 Massenet opera
34 Donned
36 Oaters
37 Book about plants
42 Radames' love
43 Dubs
44 Poe poem
45 Adhere
46 Hymn-ender
47 Adduce
48 Chela
49 Southwest wind
50 Hellions
51 Vincent Lopez theme
52 Colleen's land
53 Feather in one's cap
55 Prefix with phragm

Solution on Page 111

"Start with what you know and build on it." –Former U.S. President Bill Clinton, who apparently knows his stuff when it comes to crosswords- He uses a felt-tip pen to solve puzzles.

SOLUTIONS

EASY

	1	2	3	4	5	6	7	8	9
A	7	5	9	3	2	1	6	8	4
B	1	3	4	7	8	6	2	5	9
C	6	8	2	5	4	9	7	3	1
D	5	9	7	4	6	3	1	2	8
E	2	1	8	9	5	7	4	6	3
F	4	6	3	8	1	2	5	9	7
G	9	7	1	6	3	5	8	4	2
H	3	4	5	2	7	8	9	1	6
I	8	2	6	1	9	4	3	7	5

Answer to Sudoku Stumper: 1857

"The art of simplicity is a puzzle of complexity."

-Doug Horton

MODERATE

	1	2	3	4	5	6	7	8	9
A	9	8	7	4	2	3	5	6	1
B	2	1	4	9	5	6	7	3	8
C	6	5	3	1	8	7	9	2	4
D	1	9	5	2	3	4	6	8	7
E	3	2	6	7	9	8	4	1	5
F	4	7	8	6	1	5	3	9	2
G	5	4	9	8	6	2	1	7	3
H	8	3	1	5	7	9	2	4	6
I	7	6	2	3	4	1	8	5	9

Answer to Sudoku Stumper: 35

The first newspaper to publish a Sudoku puzzle in the U.S. was The Conway Daily Sun *in New Hampshire, in 2004.*

SOLUTIONS

DIFFICULT

	1	2	3	4	5	6	7	8	9
A	5	1	4	3	2	8	6	9	7
B	6	8	3	1	9	7	4	2	5
C	7	9	2	5	4	6	8	3	1
D	3	4	9	2	1	5	7	8	6
E	1	2	6	8	7	3	9	5	4
F	8	7	5	9	6	4	3	1	2
G	2	6	8	7	5	9	1	4	3
H	9	5	7	4	3	1	2	6	8
I	4	3	1	6	8	2	5	7	9

In 2006, British Airways forbid its flight attendants from doing Sudoku puzzles during takeoff and landing.

Answer to Sudoku Stumper: 666

EXPERT

	1	2	3	4	5	6	7	8	9
A	6	7	8	4	1	5	9	3	2
B	5	2	1	8	3	9	4	7	6
C	3	4	9	7	6	2	5	1	8
D	7	8	3	9	4	1	6	2	5
E	9	6	5	2	7	3	1	8	4
F	2	1	4	6	5	8	3	9	7
G	1	5	6	3	8	7	2	4	9
H	8	3	2	5	9	4	7	6	1
I	4	9	7	1	2	6	8	5	3

A 2008 Australian drug-related trial was aborted when it was discovered that five of the twelve jurors had been playing Sudoku instead of listening to the evidence.

Answer to Sudoku Stumper: 99

Tub Trivia

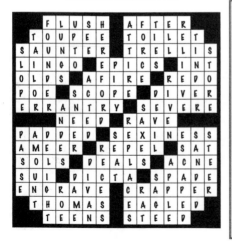

C	E	D	E		S	T	E	A	D		S	P	E	D
A	W	O	L		C	A	R	T	E		Q	U	A	I
R	E	N	E		A	L	A	R	M		U	R	S	A
	R	E	V	O	L	U	T	I	O	N	A	R	Y	
		A	N	D	S			N	O	W				
A	N	I	T	A	S		P	A	I	D		C	A	M
C	A	R	O	L		S	A	G	A		P	A	G	E
C	H	A	R	L	O	T	T	E	C	O	R	D	A	Y
R	U	T	S		V	A	T	S		P	E	E	V	E
A	M	E		V	E	R	Y		D	E	F	T	E	R
	J	A	R			C	A	R	E					
	J	E	A	N	P	A	U	L	M	A	R	A	T	
M	U	D	D		A	T	L	A	S		R	I	O	T
U	R	G	E		S	N	A	R	E		E	D	N	A
D	Y	E	D		S	O	R	E	L		D	E	E	P

> "Puzzles are like songs- A good puzzle can give you all the pleasure of being duped that a mystery story can. It has surface innocence, surprise, the revelation of a concealed meaning, and the catharsis of solution."
> —Stephen Sondheim

Bathroom Last and First

	F	L	U	S	H		A	F	T	E	R	
	T	O	U	P	E	E		T	O	I	L	E	T
S	A	U	N	T	E	R		T	R	E	L	L	I	S
L	I	N	G	O		E	P	I	C	S		I	N	T
O	L	D	S		A	F	I	R	E		R	E	D	O
P	O	E		S	C	O	P	E		D	I	V	E	R
E	R	R	A	N	T	R	Y		S	E	V	E	R	E
		N	E	E	D		R	A	V	E				
P	A	D	D	E	D		S	E	X	I	N	E	S	S
A	M	E	E	R		R	E	P	E	L		S	A	T
S	O	L	S		D	E	A	L	S		A	C	N	E
S	U	I		D	I	C	T	A		S	P	A	D	E
E	N	G	R	A	V	E		C	R	A	P	P	E	R
	T	H	O	M	A	S		E	A	G	L	E	D	
	T	E	E	N	S		S	T	E	E	D			

> "When I was hired *at* The New York Times, I would measure my mental alertness by picking up a ballpoint pen with one hand and a lit cigarette with the other. If I could finish both at the same time, I knew I was on the ball. After I quit smoking, it became harder to measure my mental powers."
> —Russell Baker, Pulitzer Prize-winning author

Rub A Dub Dub

An old M*A*S*H sitcom episode titled "38 Across" had the entire camp trying to solve a crossword puzzle. Stumped on a five-letter word for "Yiddish bedbug", a crossword whiz was brought to camp via aircraft carrier to provide the answer- "finf".

The "First" Bathroom

The amount of squares in this crossword puzzle is equal to those on a Scrabble board- 225.

THE BATHROOM LIBRARY

The Bathroom Baseball Book

•

The Bathroom Bloopers Book

•

The Bathroom Brain Teasers Book

•

The Bathroom Football Book

•

The Bathroom Funny Pages

•

The Bathroom Game Book

•

The Bathroom Golf Book

•

The Bathroom Joke Book

•

The Bathroom LOL Book

•

The Bathroom Sports Pages

•

The Bathroom Sports Quiz Book

•

The Bathroom Trivia Book

•

The Bathroom Trivia Digest

•

The Bathroom Trivia Quiz Book